KU-167-207

GO!

STOP

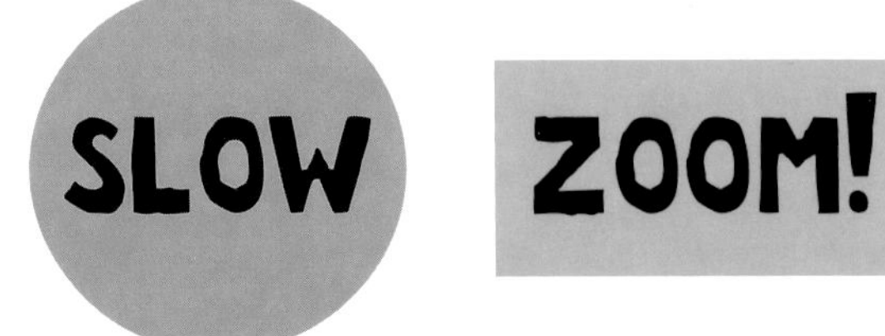
SLOW
ZOOM!

!

Beep!

GO!

STOP
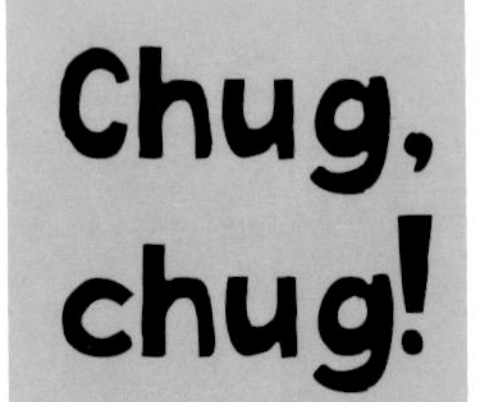
Chug,
chug!

3

GO

22

Illustrated by Paula Knight
Written by Grace Swanton

- Pull out your poster and put it up where your child can clearly see it.
- Encourage your child to talk about the vehicles with you.
- Ask your child to match each picture sticker with the correct page.
- Always reward your child with praise.

First published by Parragon in 2010

Parragon
Queen Street House
4 Queen Street
Bath BA1 1HE, UK

ISBN 978-1-4075-8925-1

Printed in China

My first vehicles book

Illustrated by Paula Knight
Written by Grace Swanton

- Pull out your poster and put it up where your child can clearly see it.
- Encourage your child to talk about the vehicles with you.
- Ask your child to match each picture sticker with the correct page.
- Always reward your child with praise.

First published by Parragon in 2010

Parragon
Queen Street House
4 Queen Street
Bath BA1 1HE, UK

ISBN 978-1-4075-8925-1

Printed in China

My first vehicles book

Parragon

Bath • New York • Singapore • Hong Kong • Cologne • Delhi • Melbourne

car

This **racing car** is in first place.

Go on, driver,
win the race!

bike

This **bike** has a bell
to ring.

What colour is the bike's bell?

miaow!

Watch out, cat!
Ring-a-ting-ting!

fire engine

This **fire engine** needs a crew.

They'll put out fires
and rescue you.

tractor

Tractors have big, chunky wheels.

They're great for driving over fields.

train

The **train** goes choo-choo
down the track.

Can you do a
choo-choo back?

boat

The **boats** rock gently on the sea.

How many **boats**?
One, two...three!

digger

A long arm stretches
from the **digger**.

Dig, dig, dig!
The hole gets bigger.

bus

We're on a **bus** ride
to go shopping.

Here's the **bus** stop.
Are we stopping?

lorry

Lorries carry heavy loads.

They drive all day
along the roads.

motorbike

This **motorbike** is very fast!

Give a wave as it zooms past.

aeroplane

What's that flying in the sky?
It can go up really high!